Movie Hits For Intermediate I

FILM TUNES
You've Always Wanted To Play

CHESTER MUSIC
part of The Music Sales Group

Exclusive Distributors: Music Sales Limited, Newmarket Road, Bury St Edmunds, Suffolk IP33 3YB
This book © Copyright 2000 Chester Music
ISBN 978-0-7119-7957-4
Order No. CH61688
Compiled by Lucy Holliday
Cover design by Chloë Alexander

ALADDIN
A Whole New World

(from Walt Disney Pictures'"Aladdin")
Words by Tim Rice Music by Alan Menken

Moderately

7

9

BABE
Pizzicati from Sylvia

Leo Delibes

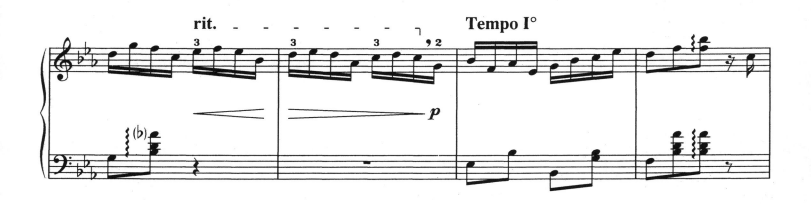

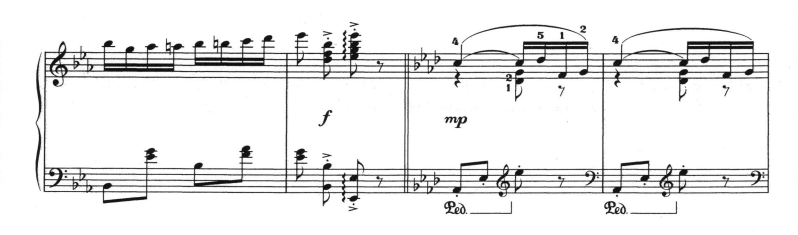

Beauty And The Beast

(from Walt Disney Pictures' "Beauty And The Beast")
Words by Howard Ashman
Music by Alan Menken

BREAKFAST AT TIFFANY'S
Moon River

Words by Johnny Mercer
Music by Henry Mancini

Moderately

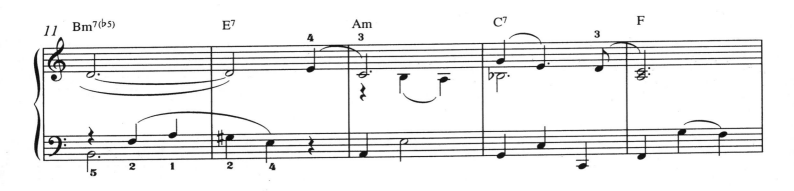

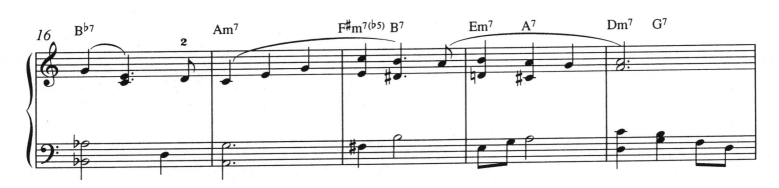

Brideshead Revisited

By Geoffrey Burgon

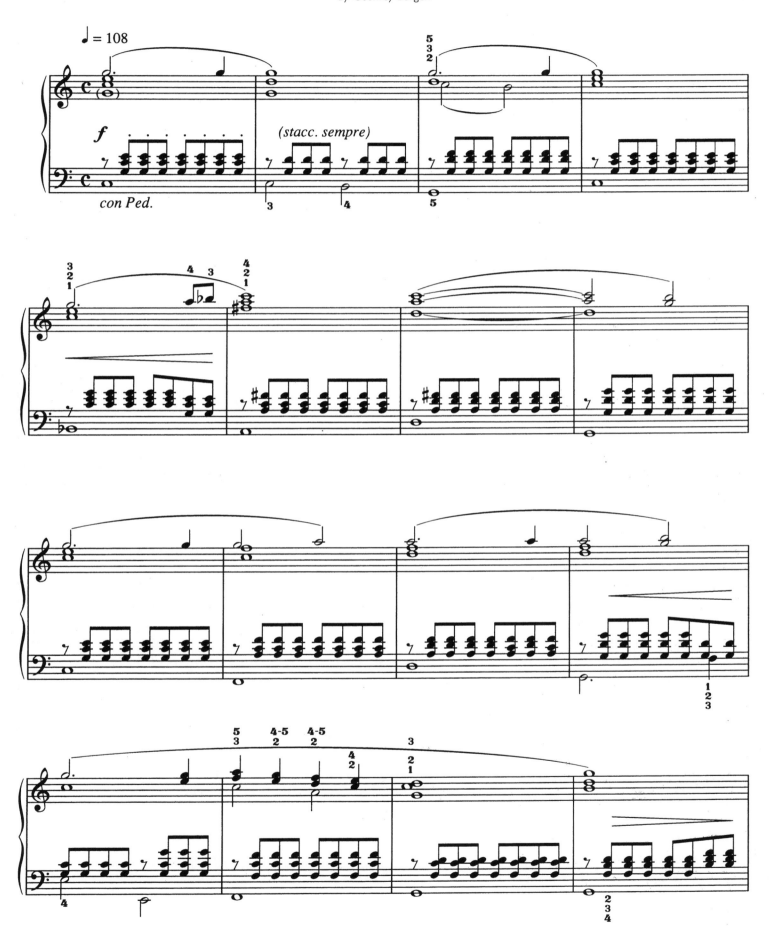

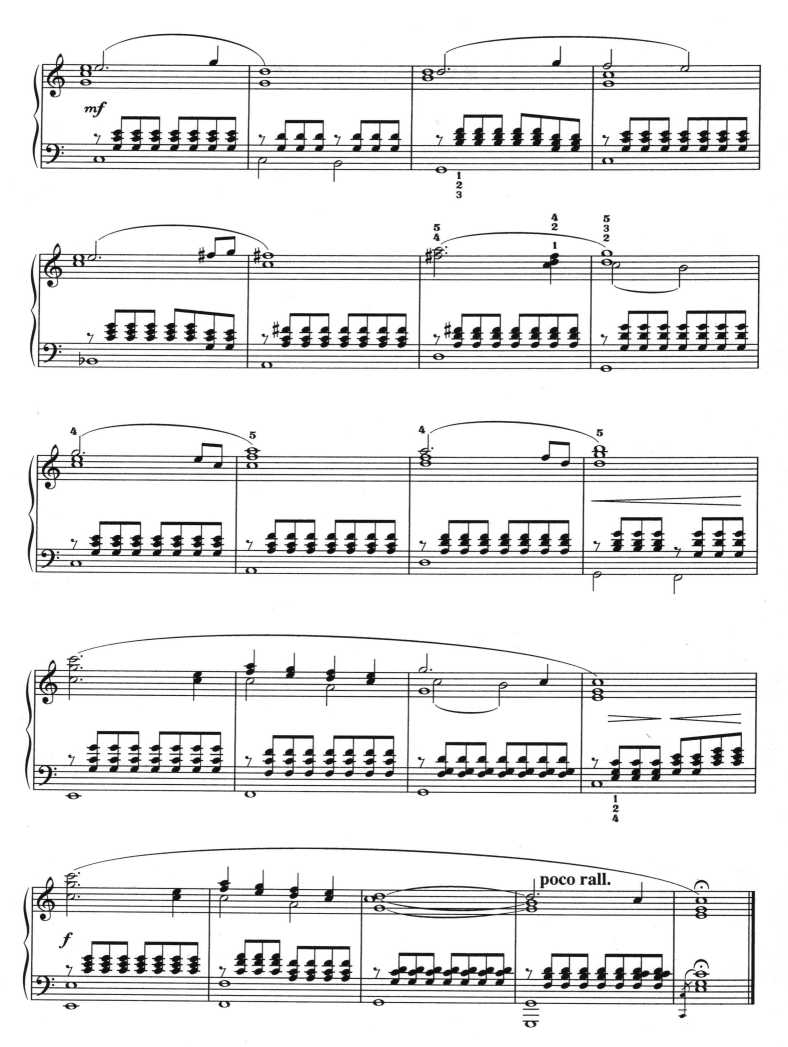

Raindrops Keep Falling on My Head

Words and Music by Burt Bacharach and Hal David

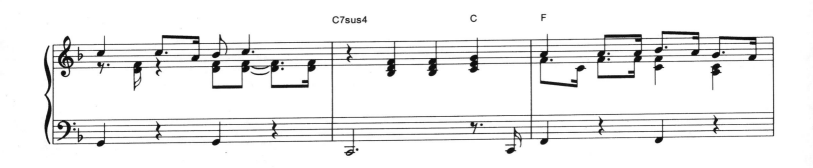

CASABLANCA
As Time Goes By

Words and Music by Herman Hupfeld

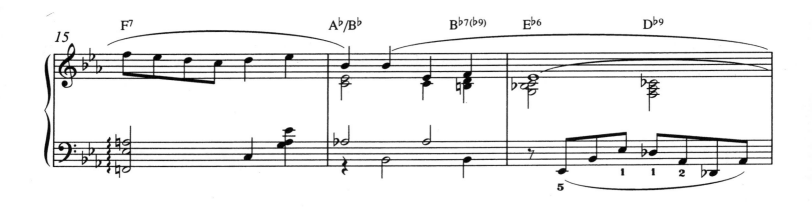

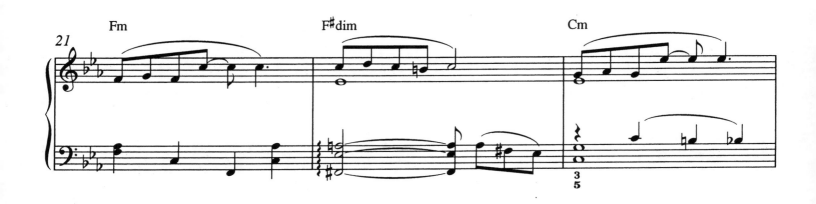

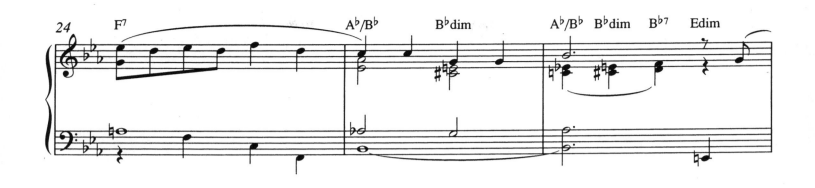

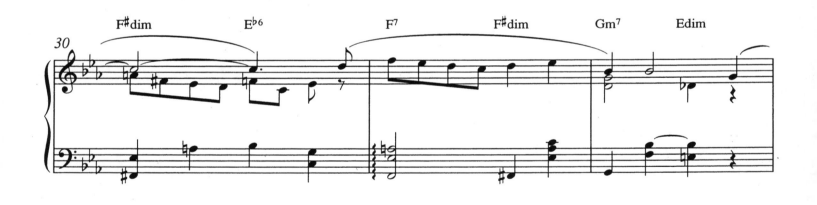

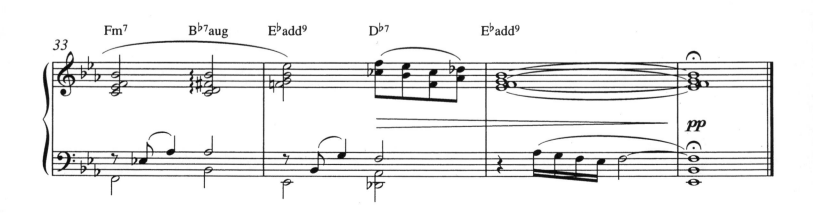

THE COMMITMENTS
Try A Little Tenderness

Words and music by Harry Woods, Jimmy Campbell and Reg Connelly

28

Theme From "E.T. (The Extra-Terrestrial)"

By John Williams

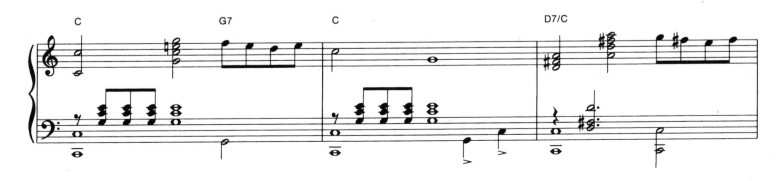

Born To Be Wild

Words & Music by Mars Bonfire

Medium Rock (♩ = 134)

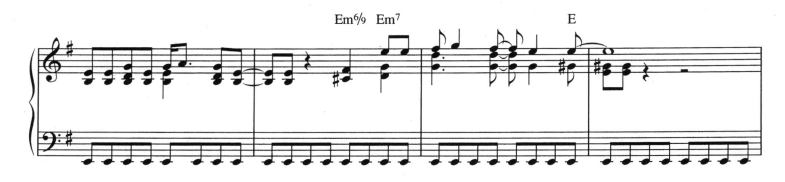

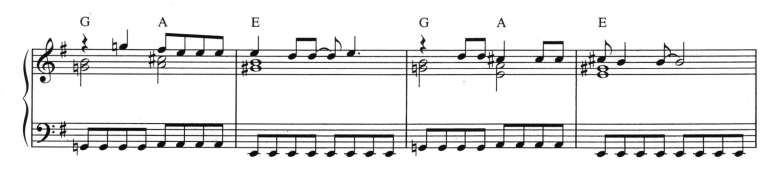

The English Patient

By Gabriel Yared

Plaintively

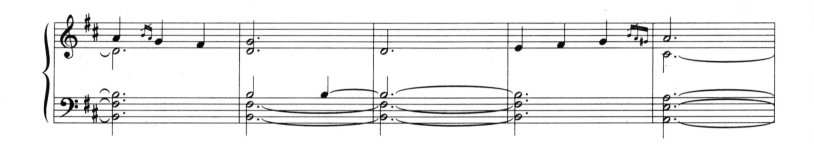

Largo from Serse

By George Frederic Handel

Un Bel Dí Vedremo
from Madame Butterfly

By Giacomo Puccini

Andante molto calmo (♩ = c.42)

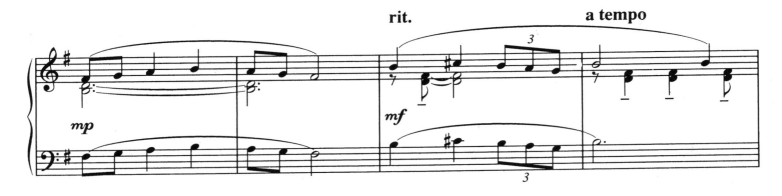

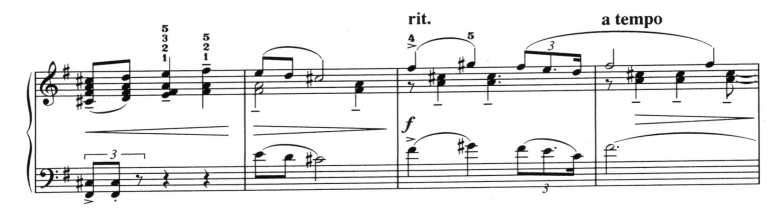

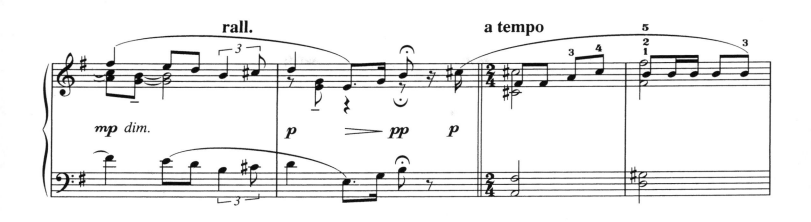

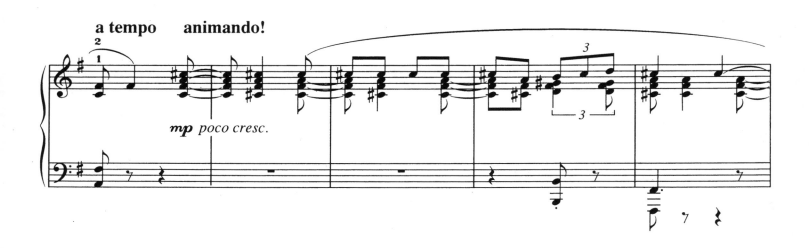

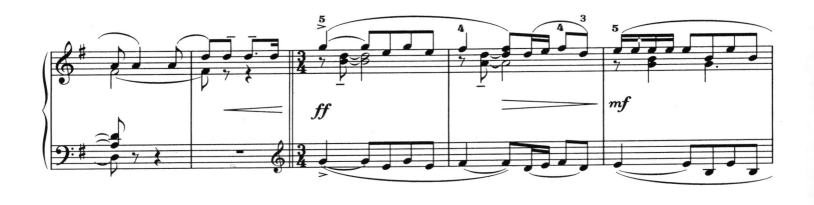

44

Wedding March
from A Midsummer Night's Dream

By Felix Mendelssohn

For All Mankind –
Theme From "Gandhi"

By Ravi Shankar & George Fenton

cresc. poco a poco

_f_

_mf_

1.2. *To next strain* 3.4.etc. *Repeat ad lib and fade*

50

Ghost

By Maurice Jarre

Expressively

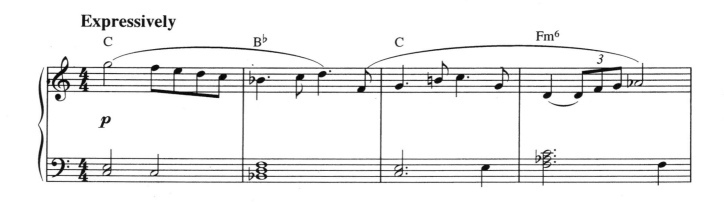

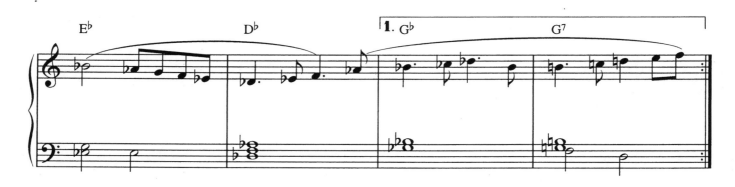

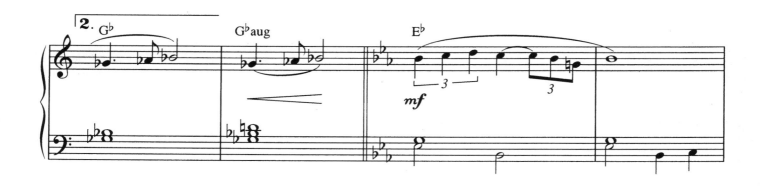

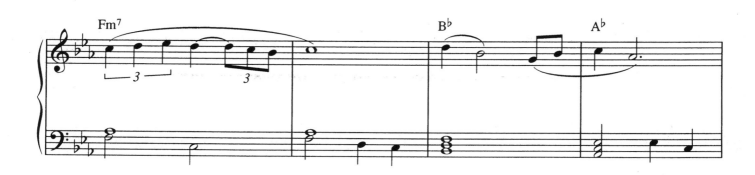

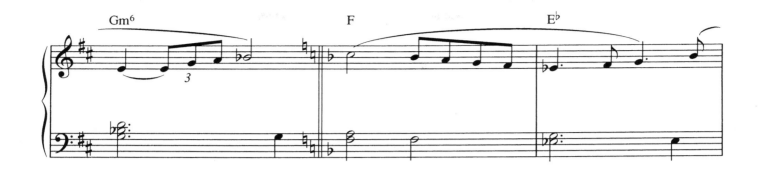

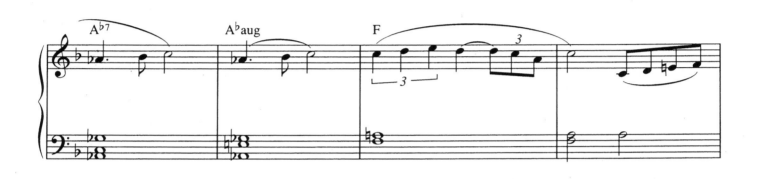

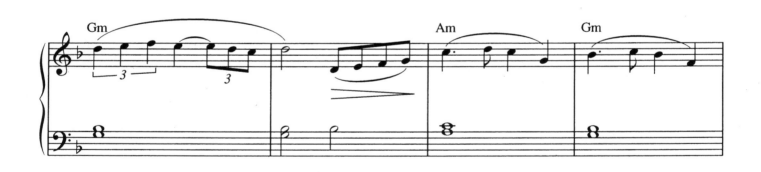

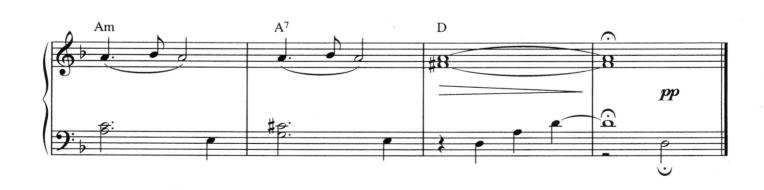

THE GODFATHER
Love Theme from "The Godfather"

By Nino Rota

Slowly and expressively

56

My Own True Love (Tara's Theme)

Words and Music by Max Steiner and Mack David

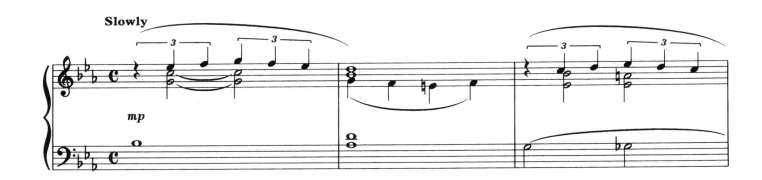

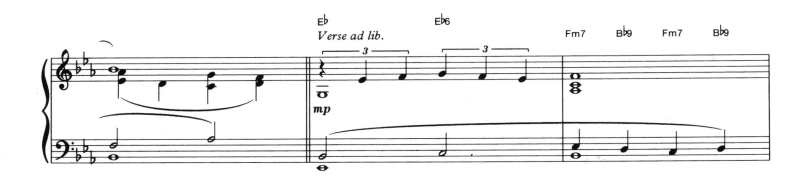

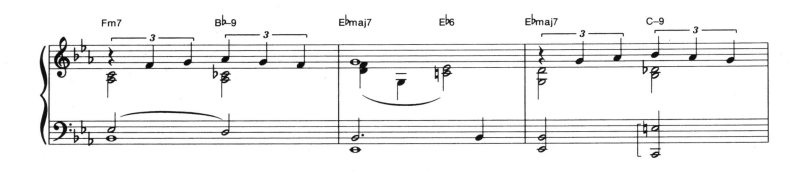

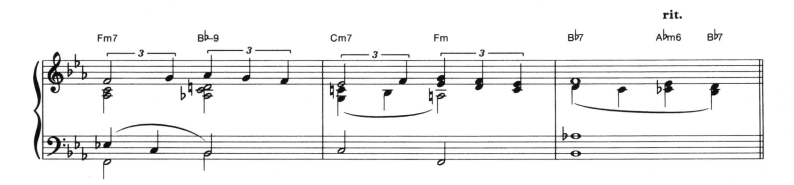

JAWS
Jaws (Theme)

By John Williams

THE JUNGLE BOOK

I Wan'na Be Like You
(from Walt Disney Pictures' "The Jungle Book")

Words & Music by Richard M. Sherman & Robert B. Sherman

Theme from "Jurassic Park"
By John Williams

66

Lawrence Of Arabia

By Maurice Jarre

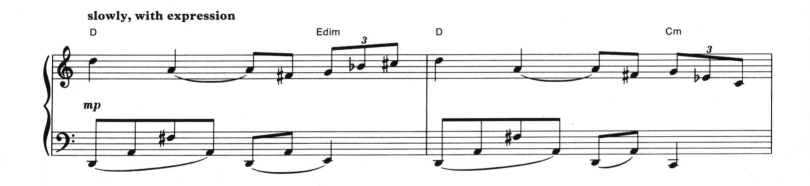

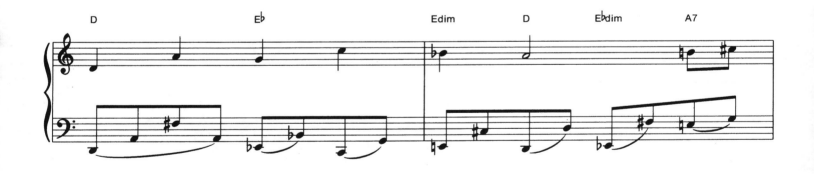

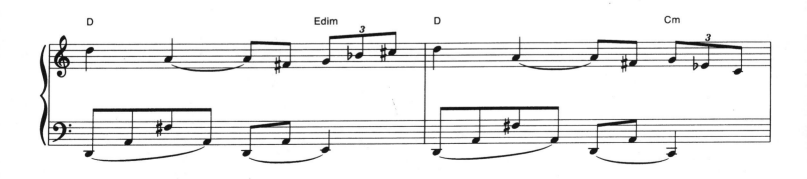

71

Live And Let Die

Words & Music by Paul & Linda McCartney

73

Theme From "Mission: Impossible"

By Lalo Schifrin

The Mission

By Ennio Morricone

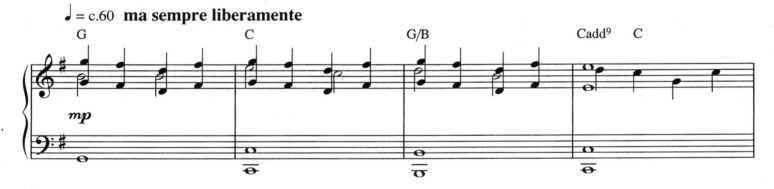

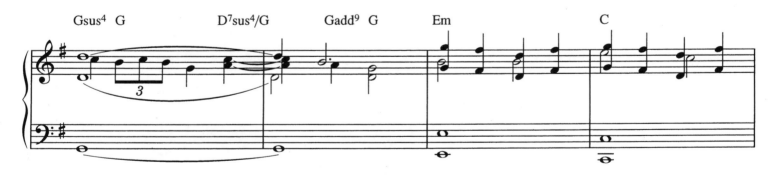

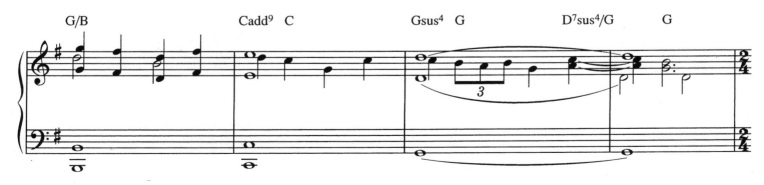

The Heart Asks Pleasure First
(The Promise/The Sacrifice)

By Michael Nyman

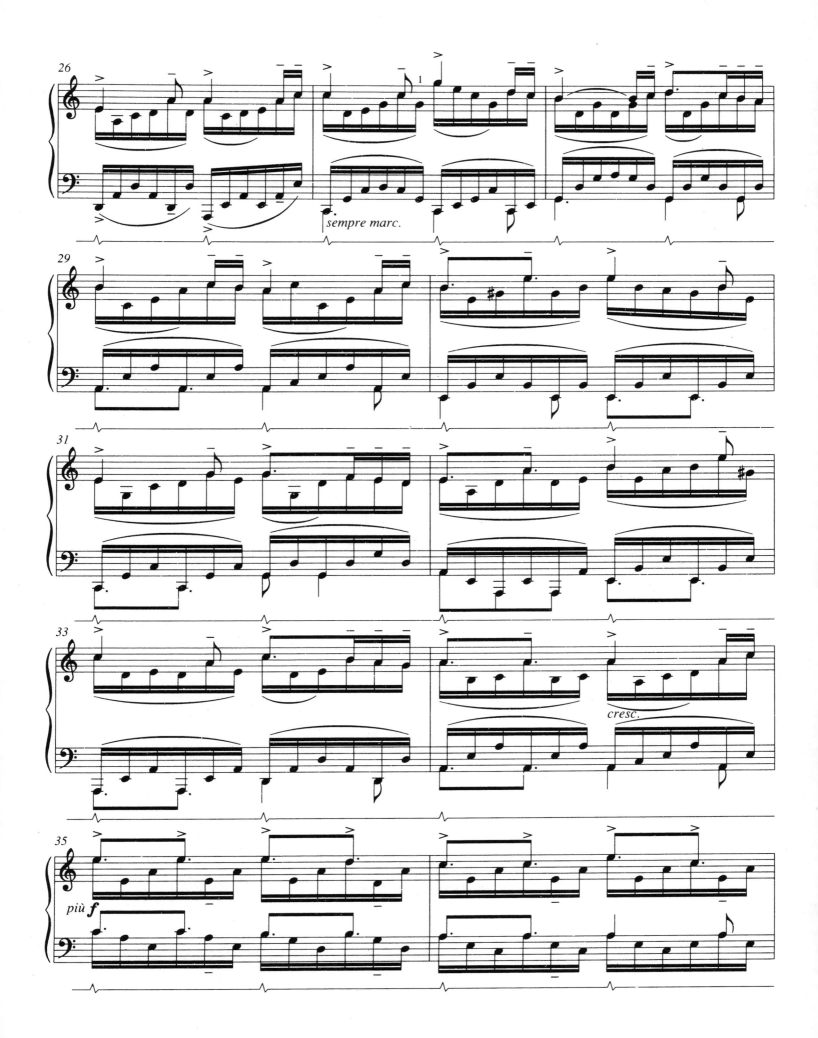

POCAHONTAS

Colors Of The Wind
(from Walt Disney Pictures' "Pocahontas")

Music by Alan Menken
Lyrics by Stephen Schwartz

82

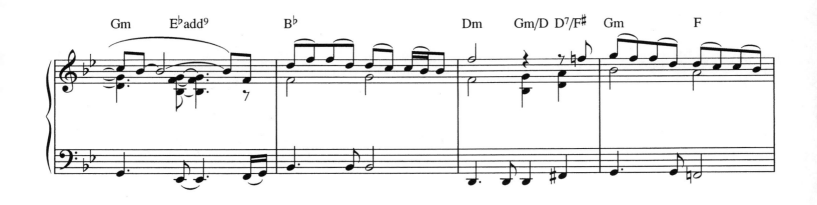

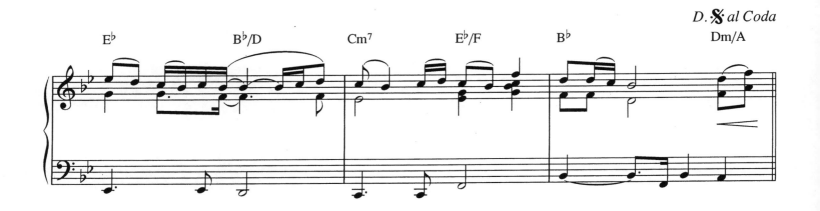

Psycho (Prelude)

By Bernard Herrmann

Raiders March

By John Williams

With movement

Schindler's List

By John Williams

95

SEVEN

Air On The 'G' String

By Johann Sebastian Bach

Lento, poco rubato (♩ = c.48)

Molto rall.

Aria from Goldberg Variations

Adagio (♩ = 66)

Weep You No More, Sad Fountains

By Patrick Doyle

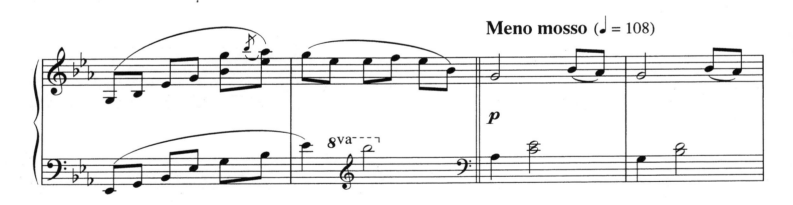

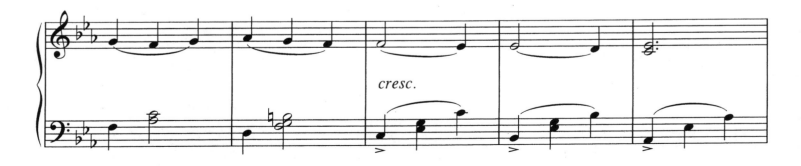

Più mosso

rall.

Theme from "Star Trek
(The Motion Picture)"

By Jerry Goldsmith

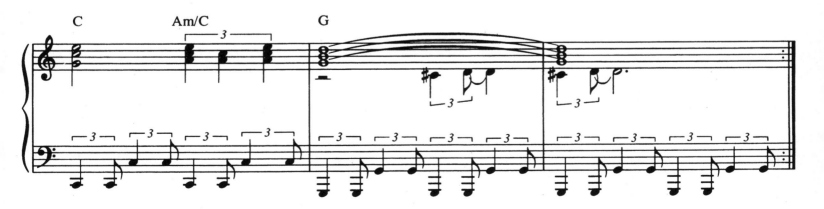

105

The Good, The Bad And The Ugly

By Ennio Morricone

Moderato, ♩ = 104

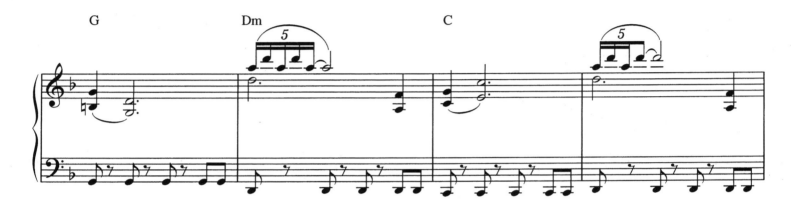

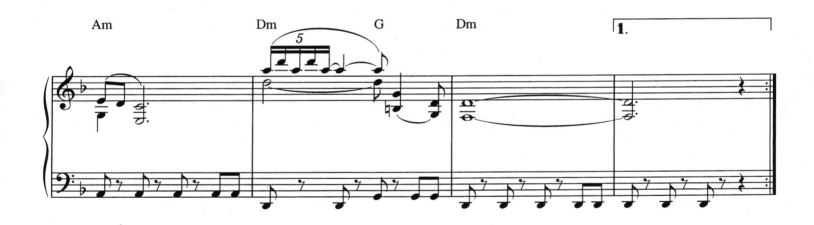

108

TITANIC
My Heart Will Go On
(Love Theme from "Titanic")

Words and Music by Will Jennings and James Horner

113

The Flower Duet from Lakmé

By Leo Delibes

THE UNTOUCHABLES

Vesti La Giubba from I Pagliacci

By Ruggiero Leoncavallo

117

Bright Eyes
Words & Music Mike Batt

Fairly slowly with expression

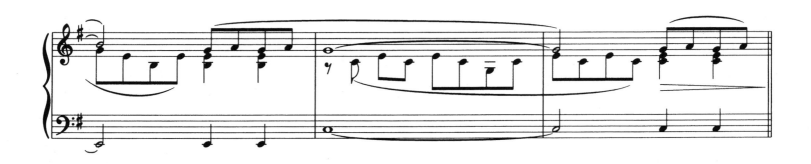

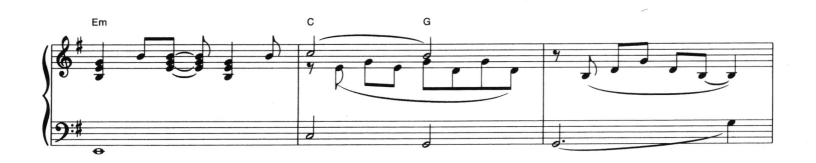

THE WIZARD OF OZ
Over The Rainbow

Words and Music by E.Y. Harburg and Harold Arlen

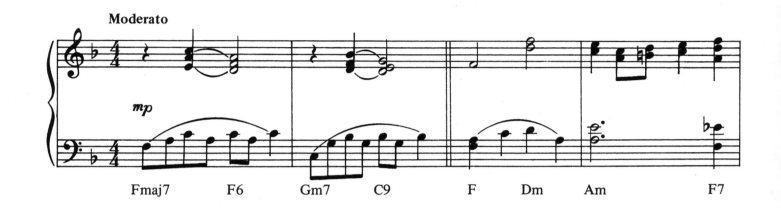

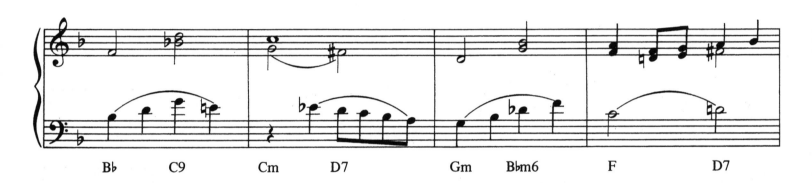

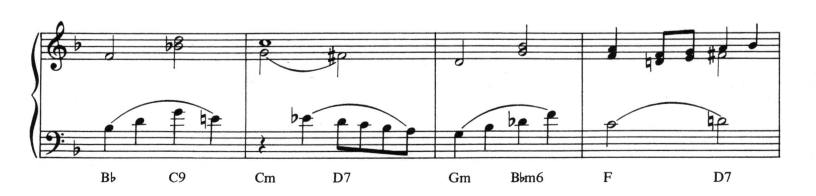

THE WITCHES OF EASTWICK
Nessun Dorma
from Turandot

By Giacomo Puccini

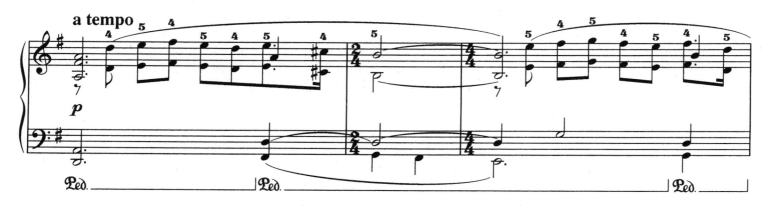

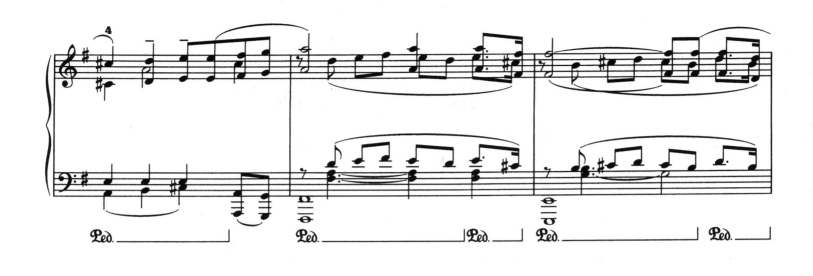

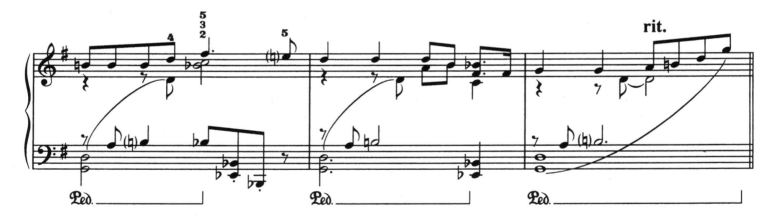

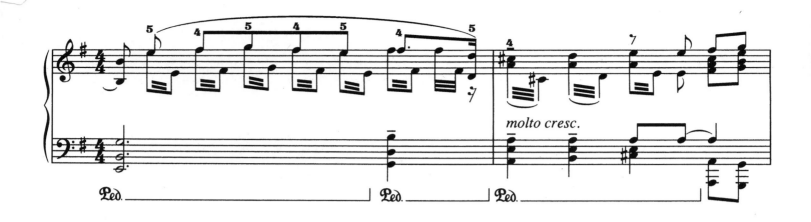

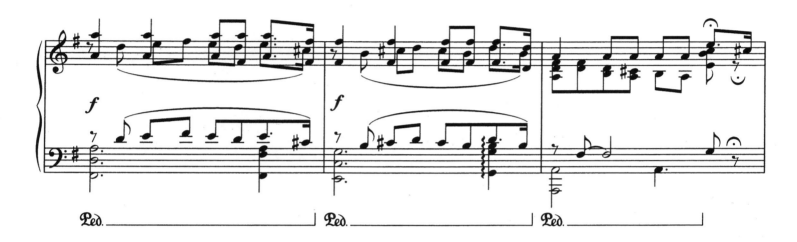

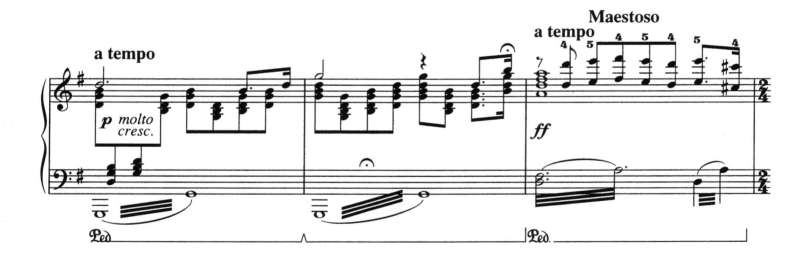

126

Printed in the EU.   12/09 (172317)

If you like this book you will also like these for solo piano

CLASSIC ADS
22 classic themes and music made popular by T.V. adverts.
Includes: Adagio for Strings (The Times), 633 Squadron (Zurich), Johnny and Mary (Renault Clio), Fields of Gold (Cancer Research).
Order No. CH65989

MOVIE HITS YOU'VE ALWAYS WANTED TO PLAY
30 of the best known themes and songs from the greatest films arranged for intermediate solo piano.
Includes: American Beauty, Chocolat, Crouching Tiger Hidden Dragon, Moulin Rouge, and many more.
Order No. CH65439

CLASSICAL CHILLOUT
Sit down at the piano and chill out with some of the world's most soothing melodies.
Includes: Clair de Lune (Debussy), Gymnopédie No.1 (Satie), Sarabande in D minor (Handel) and The Heart Asks Pleasure First from "The Piano" (Nyman).
Order No. CH64053

CLASSICAL CHILLOUT GOLD
Unwind with this great sequel to our best selling *classical chillout* containing 29 super cool piano favourites to play and enjoy.
Includes: Adagio for Strings (Barber), The Lamb (Tavener), Pavane (Fauré)
Order No. CH66319

THE GOLD SERIES
A beautifully presented series of albums containing the most famous masterpieces from the world's greatest composers.

MOZART GOLD
Includes: A Musical Joke, Piano Concerto No.21 'Elvira Madigan', Serenade in B♭ 'Gran Partita' and Symphony No.40 in G minor.
Order No. CH65505

BEETHOVEN GOLD
Includes: Symphony No.5, Für Elise, Minuet in G and the 'Moonlight' Sonata.
Order No. CH65670

CHOPIN GOLD
Includes: All famous waltzes, nocturnes, preludes and mazurkas as well as excerpts from Piano Concerto No.1, Ballade in G minor and Sonata No.2 in B♭ Minor.
Order No. CH65681

TCHAIKOVSKY GOLD
Includes: 1812 Overture, plus music from The Nutcracker, Sleeping Beauty and Swan Lake.
Order No. CH65692

For more information on these and the thousands of other titles available from Chester Music and Music Sales, please contact:

Music Sales Limited
Newmarket Road, Bury St Edmunds, Suffolk, IP33 3YB, UK
www.musicsales.com